High-Frequency
READERS™

Take-Home Books

Copyright © 2000 by Scholastic Inc.
SCHOLASTIC, HIGH-FREQUENCY READERS, and associated logos and designs are
trademarks and/or registered trademarks of Scholastic Inc.
All rights reserved. Published by Scholastic Inc.
Printed in the U.S.A.
ISBN 0-439-09059-8

4 5 6 7 8 9 10   40   05 04 03 02 01 00

Table of Contents

About Scholastic
High-Frequency Readers

These Scholastic High-Frequency Readers are blackline masters of the books your children have read in class. After you have made copies, follow the directions on the next page to make individual books for your  children. Encourage them to take home these books to share with family and friends.

You may wish to have children help fold and staple the pages of their Scholastic High-Frequency Readers. Encourage children to color the illustrations in school or at home to create their own unique books.

Assembly Instructions

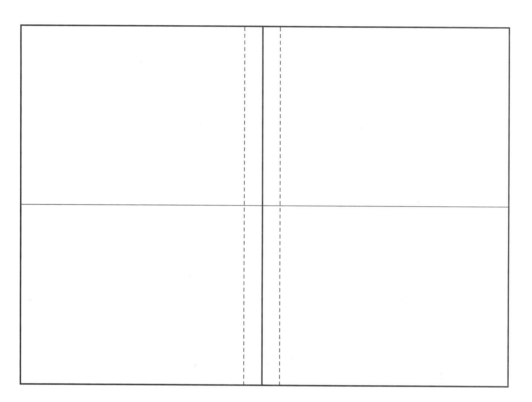

- Cut along the dotted lines

- Fold all the pages in half.

- Staple along the vertical fold ("spine").

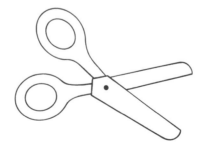

Dear Family,

From time to time your child will bring home his or her very own Scholastic High-Frequency Reader to share with family and friends. These are copies of books he or she has already read in class. With your help, these books can provide your child with important practice in reading, and a meaningful shared experience.

Some of the books are nonfiction, and some are storybooks. Each book contains words commonly found in beginning reading materials.

You may want to take some time every day to read these High-Frequency Readers with your child. Here are some suggestions you may find helpful:

- Encourage your child to join in reading the story with you.

- Read each page aloud as you run your hand under the words. Ask your child to imitate, or "echo," what he or she has just heard.

- Write words from the story on cards or slips of paper. Say a word and ask your child to point to it. Repeat with other words. Once your child feels comfortable with this task, point to the words in random order for your child to read.

- Choose one of the words you wrote and have your child find it each time it appears in the story. Ask your child to read the sentence in which it appears.

- Enjoy the books!

Sincerely,

_____

Querida familia:

En ocasiones, su niño llevará a casa su propio libro de Scholastic Cuentos de palabras frecuentes para compartir con ustedes y sus amigos. Su niño ya ha leído estos libros en clase. Sabemos que con su ayuda, los Cuentos de palabras frecuentes le darán a su niño la oportunidad de practicar y compartir la lectura con toda la familia.

Algunos libros son de cuentos y otros son realistas. Cada libro contiene palabras que normalmente se encuentran en materiales de lectura para principiantes.

Si desea leer con su niño estos Cuentos de palabras frecuentes un rato cada día, aquí le damos algunas sugerencias que le pueden ayudar:

- Anime a su niño a leer el cuento con usted.

- Lea cada página en voz alta mientras señala las palabras con su mano. Diga a su niño que imite lo que acaba de escuchar.

- Escriba las palabras de la lista en tarjetas o tiras de papel. Diga una palabra y pida a su niño que la señale. Haga lo mismo con otras palabras. Una vez que su niño se sienta cómodo con este ejercicio, señale palabras sin un orden particular para que su niño las lea.

- Escoja una de las palabras que escribió y pida a su niño que la encuentre cada vez que esa palabra aparezca en el cuento. Anímele a que lea la oración que tenga esa palabra.

- ¡Diviértase leyendo con su niño!

Atentamente,

_____

SCHOOL

Written by Gay Su Pinnell

Illustrated by Peggy Tagel

Scholastic Inc.

**New York Toronto London Auckland Sydney
Mexico City New Delhi Hong Kong**

Copyright © 2000 by Scholastic Inc.
SCHOLASTIC, HIGH-FREQUENCY READERS, and associated logos and designs are trademarks and/or registered trademarks of Scholastic Inc.
All rights reserved. Published by Scholastic Inc.
Printed in the U.S.A.

4 5 6 7 8 9 10   23   05 04 03 02 01 00

I see school.

I see crayons.

I see children.

I see scissors.

I see chairs.

I see books.

I see desks.

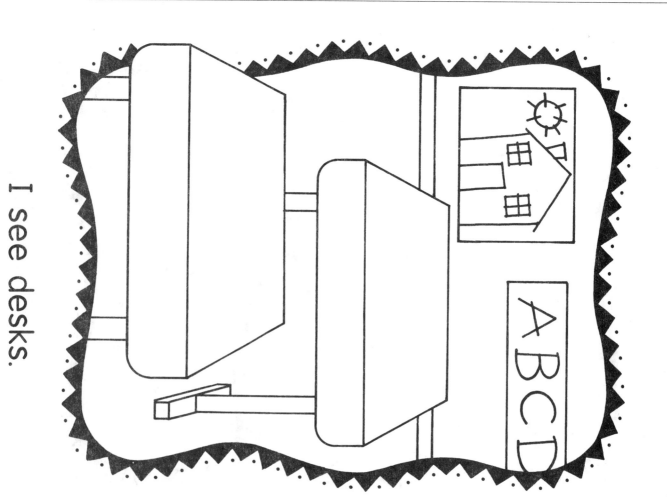

LUNCH

Written by Gay Su Pinnell

Illustrated by David Bamundo

Scholastic Inc.

New York Toronto London Auckland Sydney
Mexico City New Delhi Hong Kong

4 5 6 7 8 9 10   23   05 04 03 02 01 00

I like lunch.

I like apples.

I like milk.

I like cookies.

I like sandwiches.

I like bananas.

I like pizza.

I Like

Written by Gay Su Pinnell

Illustrated by Lauren Scheuer

Scholastic Inc.

New York   Toronto   London   Auckland   Sydney
Mexico City   New Delhi   Hong Kong

4 5 6 7 8 9 10   23   05 04 03 02 0100

I like to sleep.

I like to wake up.

I like to hug.

I like to eat.

I like to ride.

I like to read.

I like to write.

I Am

Written by Adria Klein

Illustrated by Susan Gal

Scholastic Inc.

**New York Toronto London Auckland Sydney
Mexico City New Delhi Hong Kong**

I am sleeping.

I am running.

I am swinging.

I am jumping.

I am dancing.

I am building.

I am climbing.

I CAN SEE

Written by Adria Klein

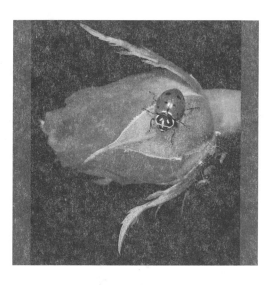

Scholastic Inc.

New York Toronto London Auckland Sydney
Mexico City New Delhi Hong Kong

No part of this publication may be reproduced in whole or in part, or stored in a retrieval system, or transmitted in any form or by any means, electronic, mechanical, photocopying, recording, or otherwise, without written permission of the publisher. For information regarding permission, write to Scholastic Inc. Education Group, 555 Broadway, New York, NY 10012.

What can you see?

I can see a **red** ladybug.

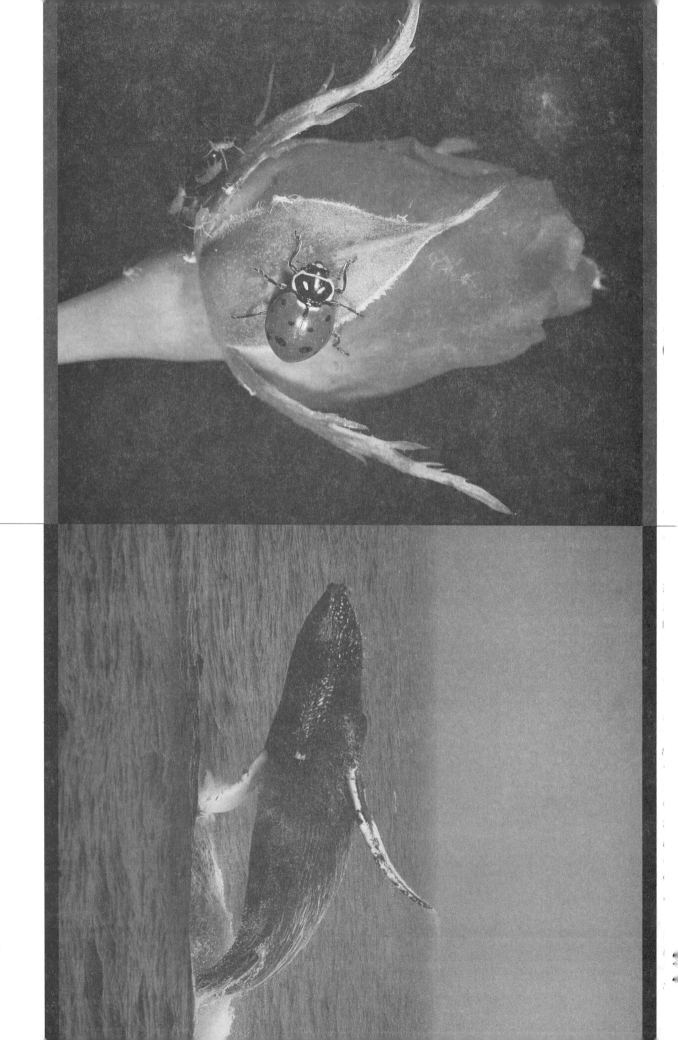

I can see a **black** whale.

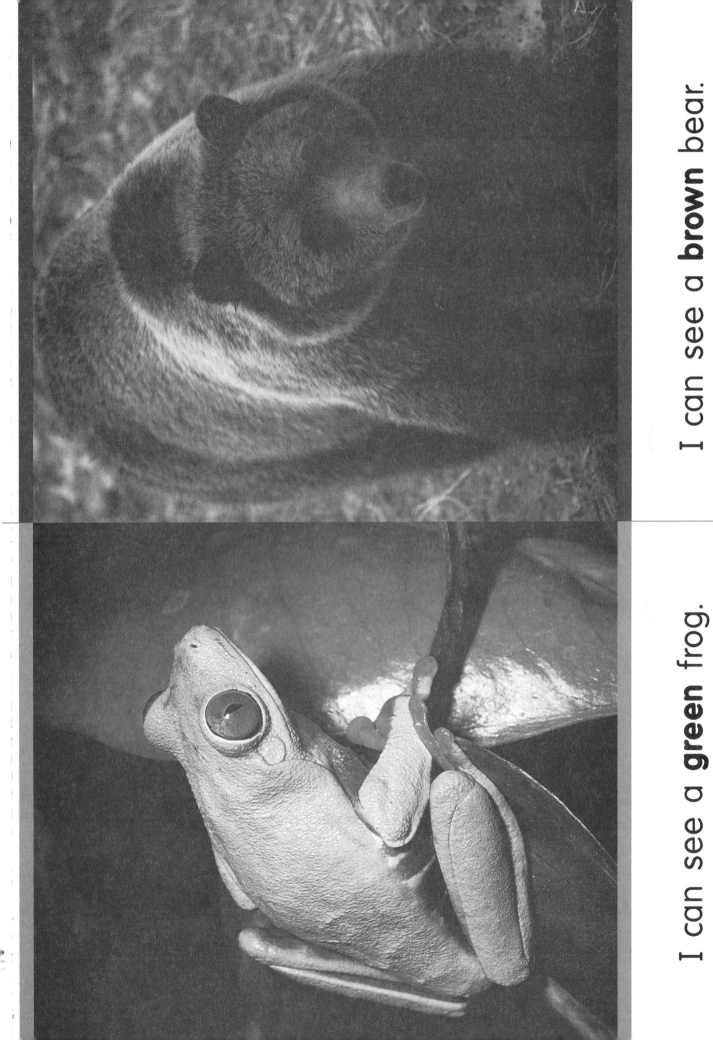

I can see a **brown** bear.

❸

I can see a **green** frog.

❻

I can see a **yellow** snake.

I can see a **gray** elephant.

Kittens

Written by Don L. Curry

Illustrated by Cynthia Jabar

Scholastic Inc.

New York Toronto London Auckland Sydney
Mexico City New Delhi Hong Kong

I can see kittens!

Can you see 1 kitten?

Can you see kittens?

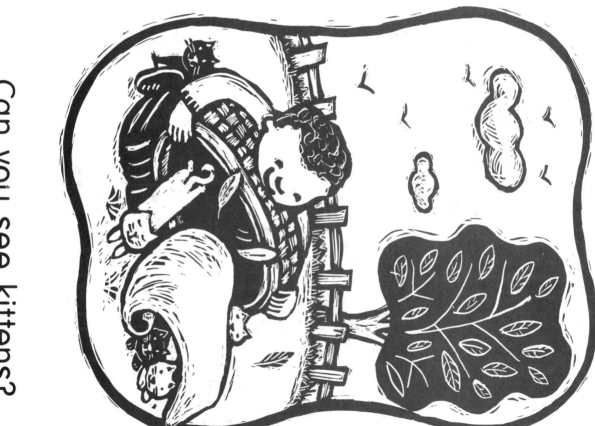

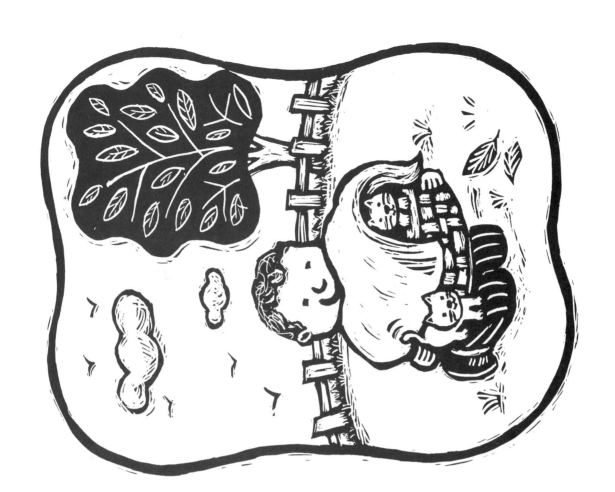

Can you see 2 kittens?

Can you see 5 kittens?

Can you see 3 kittens?

Can you see 4 kittens?

Dogs

Written by Amy Levin

Illustrated by Sue Dennen

Scholastic Inc.

New York Toronto London Auckland Sydney
Mexico City New Delhi Hong Kong

Copyright © 2000 by Scholastic Inc.
SCHOLASTIC, HIGH-FREQUENCY READERS, and associated logos and designs are trademarks and/or registered trademarks of Scholastic Inc.
All rights reserved. Published by Scholastic Inc.
Printed in the U.S.A.

4 5 6 7 8 9 10   23   05 04 03 02 0100

DOG SHOW

We like dogs!

My dog can walk.

My dog can swim.

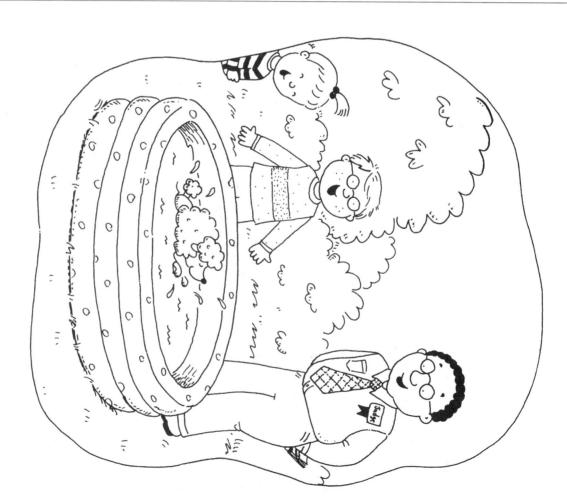

My dog can jump.

My dog can sit.

My dog can catch.

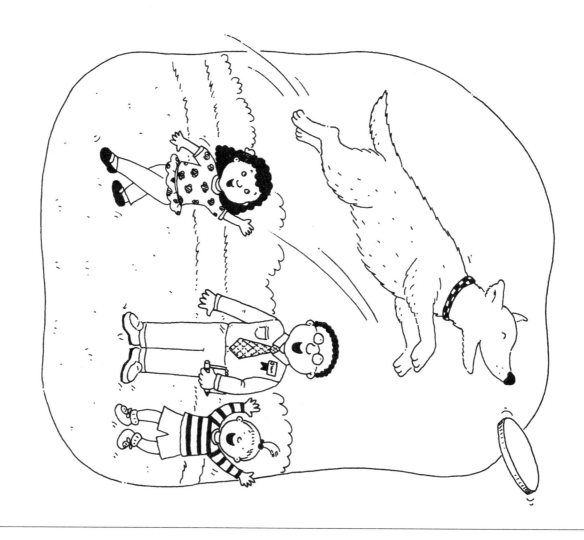

My dog can sleep.

THE BAND

Written by Nancy Leber

Illustrated by Linda Helton

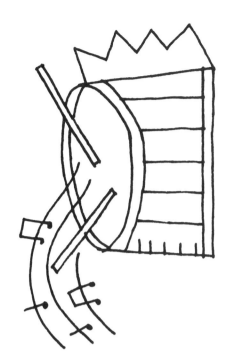

Scholastic Inc.

**New York Toronto London Auckland Sydney
Mexico City New Delhi Hong Kong**

Can you see the band?

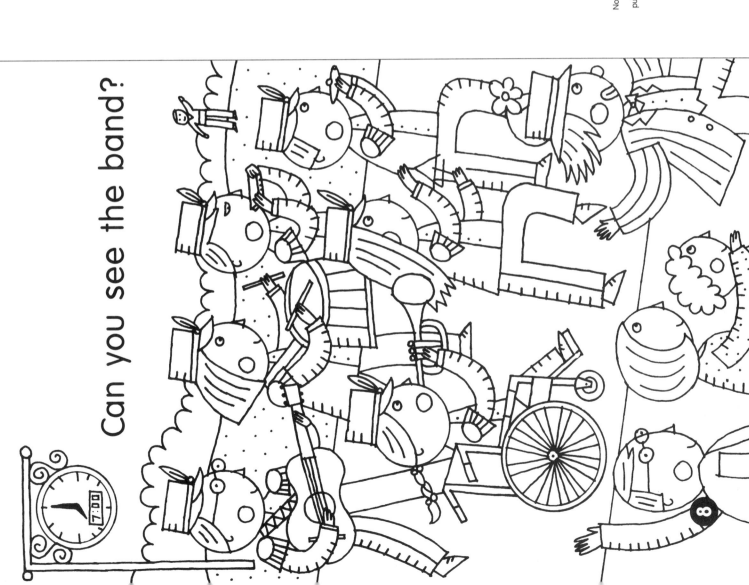

Can you see the guitar?

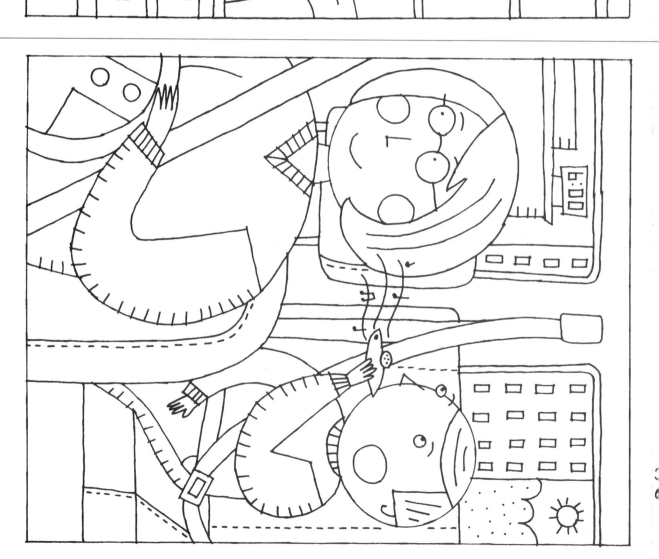

Can you see the kazoo?

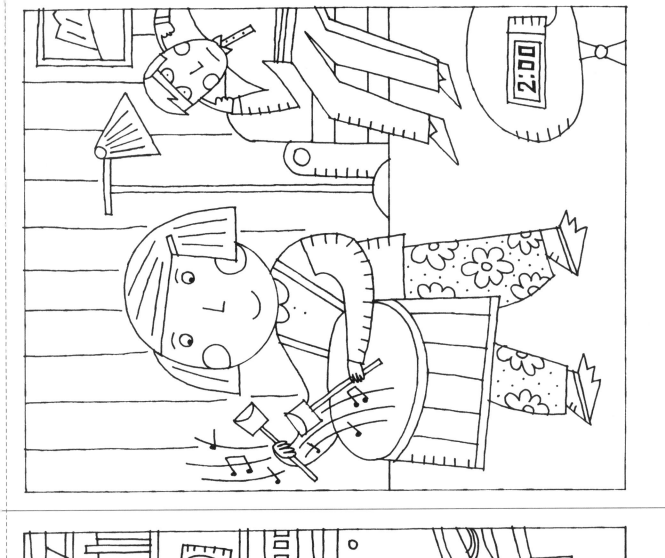

Can you see the drum?

Can you see the triangle?

Can you see the horn?

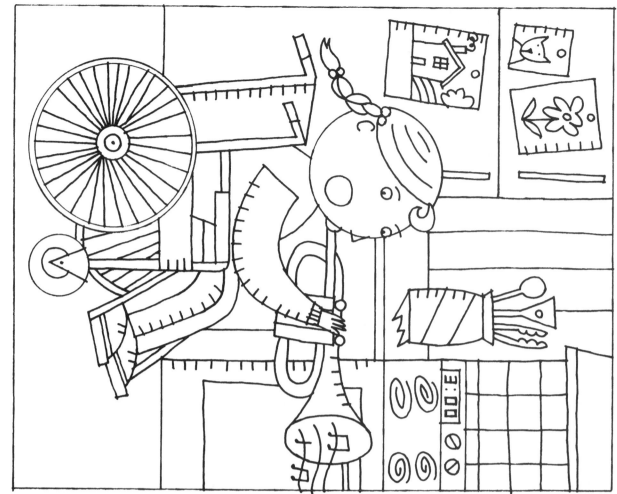

Can you see the harmonica?

We Are Painting

Written by Francie Alexander

Illustrated by Michael Grejniec

Scholastic Inc.

New York Toronto London Auckland Sydney
Mexico City New Delhi Hong Kong

4 5 6 7 8 9 10   23   05 04 03 02 01 00

1

We are painting!

8

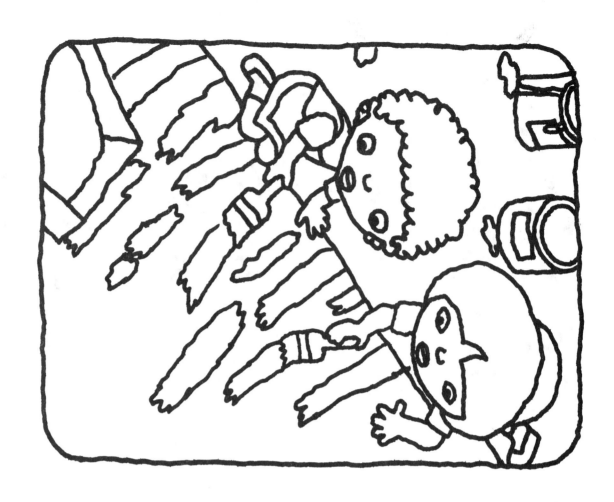

We are painting **green** grass.

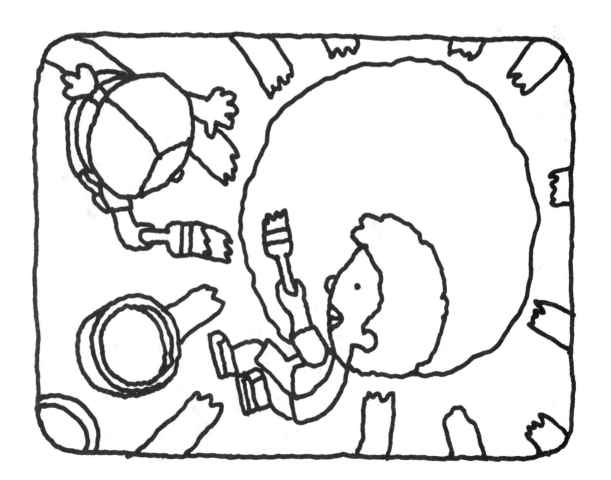

We are painting 1 **yellow** sun.

We are painting 5 **red** flowers.

We are painting 2 **black** horses.

We are painting 4 **orange** butterflies.

We are painting 3 **blue** birds.

We Can Go!

Written by Ellen Geist

Illustrated by Ken Bowser

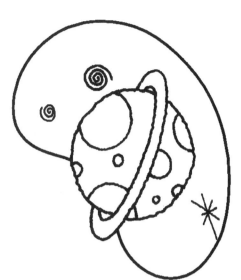

Scholastic Inc.

**New York   Toronto   London   Auckland   Sydney
Mexico City   New Delhi   Hong Kong**

4 5 6 7 8 9 10   23   05 04 03 02 01 00

We can go to the moon!

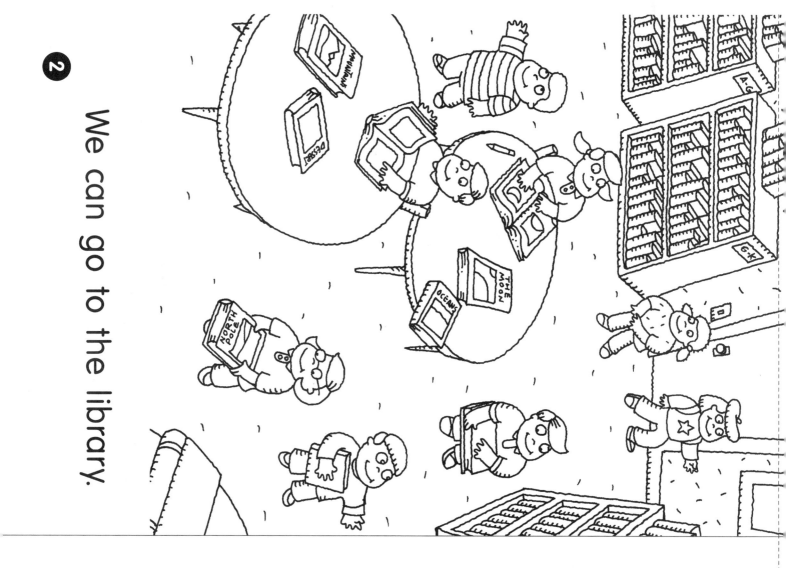

We can go to the library.

I can go to the jungle.

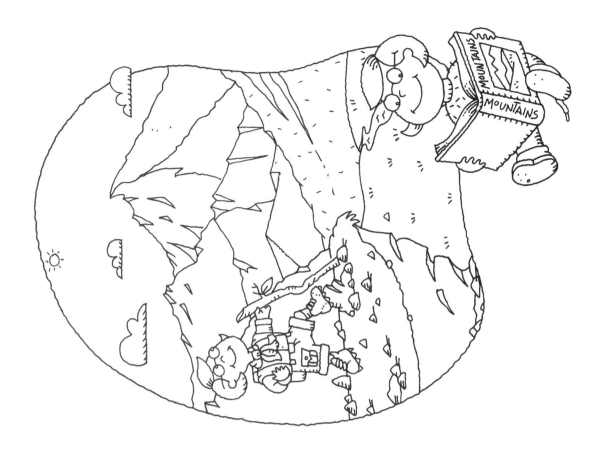

I can go to the mountains.

I can go to the ocean.

I can go to the desert.

I can go to the North Pole.

Can You See It?

Written by Cori M. Murray

Illustrated by Karen Schmidt

Scholastic Inc.

New York Toronto London Auckland Sydney
Mexico City New Delhi Hong Kong

No part of this publication may be reproduced in whole or in part, or stored in a retrieval system, or transmitted in any form or by any means, electronic, mechanical, photocopying, recording, or otherwise, without written permission of the publisher. For information regarding permission, write to Scholastic Inc., Education Group, 555 Broadway, New York, NY 10012.

1

We see animals!

8

Can you see it?
I see a rooster.

Can you see it?
I see a skunk.

2

7

Can you see it?
I see a pig.

③

Can you see it?
I see a mouse.

⑥

Can you see it?
I see a dog.

4

Can you see it?
I see a horse.

5

We Like Fruit

Written by Millen Lee

Illustrated by Tungwai Chau

Scholastic Inc.

New York   Toronto   London   Auckland   Sydney
Mexico City   New Delhi   Hong Kong

Copyright © 2000 by Scholastic Inc.
SCHOLASTIC, HIGH-FREQUENCY READERS, and associated logos and designs are
trademarks and/or registered trademarks of Scholastic Inc.
All rights reserved. Published by Scholastic Inc.
Printed in the U.S.A.

4 5 6 7 8 9 10   23   05 04 03 02 0100

We like fruit.

We go to the store.

I like bananas and strawberries.

I like apples and oranges.

Only 20¢/LB

I like peaches and bananas.

I like oranges and pears.

30¢/LB

I like pears and peaches.

Pears

My cats are on me!

My Cats

Written by Eileen Robinson

Illustrated by Diane Palmisciano

Scholastic Inc.

New York   Toronto   London   Auckland   Sydney
Mexico City   New Delhi   Hong Kong

No part of this publication may be reproduced in whole or in part, or stored in a retrieval system, or transmitted in any form or by any means, electronic, mechanical, photocopying, recording, or otherwise, without written permission of the publisher. For information regarding permission, write to Scholastic Inc., Education Group, 555 Broadway, New York, NY 10012.

Copyright © 2000 by Scholastic Inc.

SCHOLASTIC, HIGH-FREQUENCY READERS, and associated logos and designs are trademarks and/or registered trademarks of Scholastic Inc.
All rights reserved. Published by Scholastic Inc.
Printed in the U.S.A.

4 5 6 7 8 9 10   23   05 04 03 02 0100

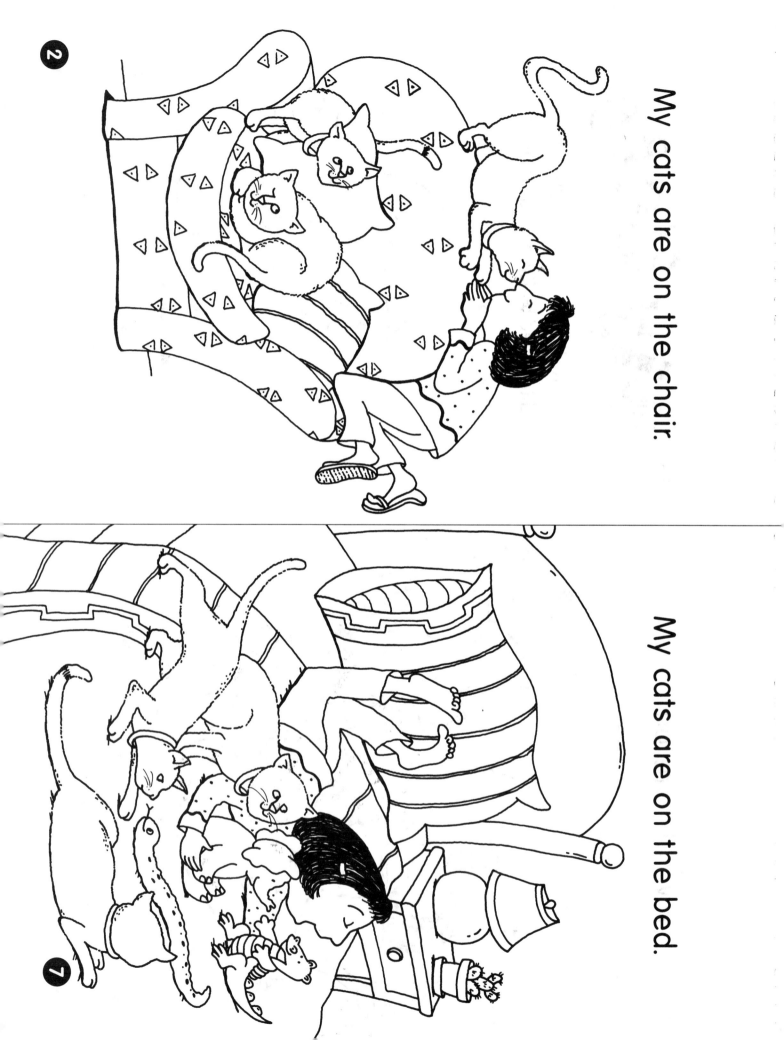

My cats are on the chair.

My cats are on the bed.

My cats are on the rug.

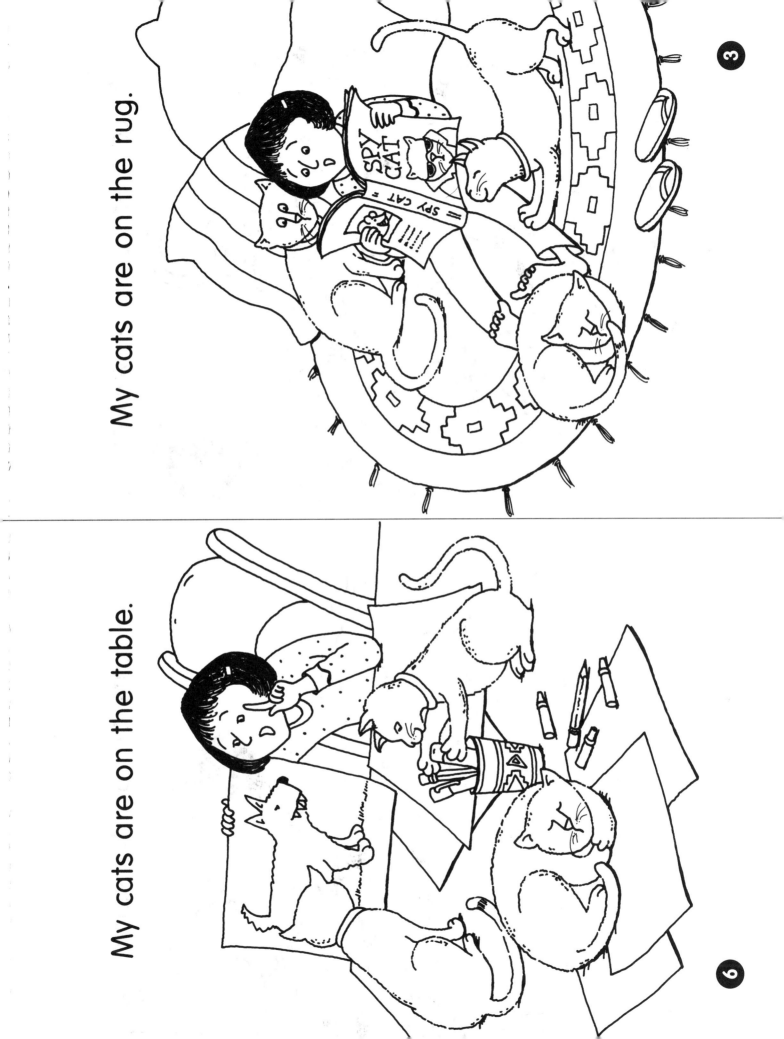

My cats are on the table.

3

6

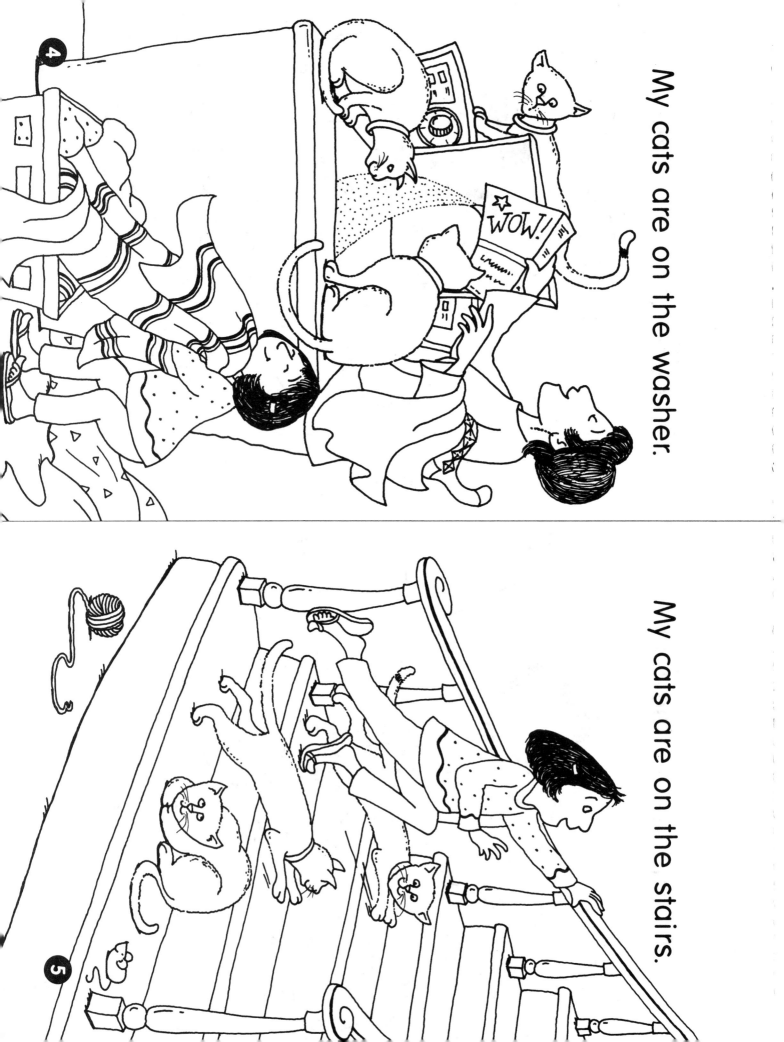

My cats are on the washer.

4

My cats are on the stairs.

5

Look!

Written by Cindy Chapman

Illustrated by Esther Szegedy

Scholastic Inc.

New York Toronto London Auckland Sydney
Mexico City New Delhi Hong Kong

Copyright © 2000 by Scholastic Inc.
SCHOLASTIC, HIGH-FREQUENCY READERS, and associated logos and designs are trademarks and/or registered trademarks of Scholastic Inc.
All rights reserved. Published by Scholastic Inc.
Printed in the U.S.A.

4 5 6 7 8 9 10   23   05 04 03 02 01 00

Look!
The dogs are in the tub.

Look!
The dogs are in the tub.

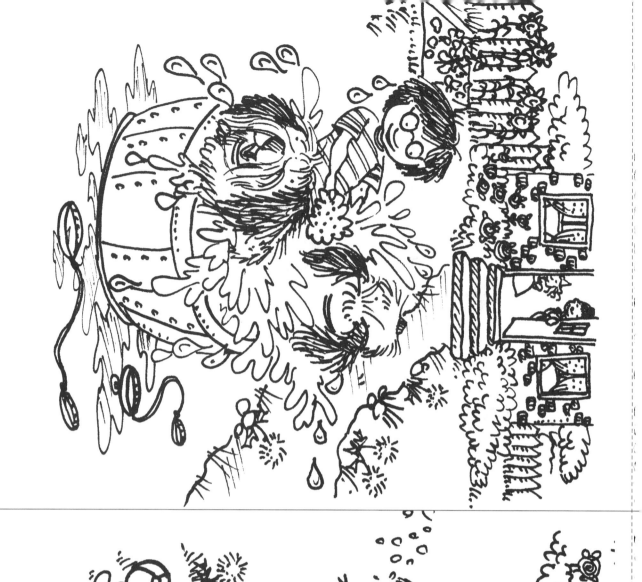

Look!
The dogs are in the sand.

Look!
The dogs are in the garden.

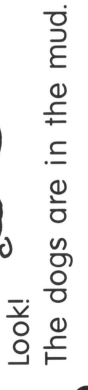

Look!
The dogs are in the mud.

Look!
The dogs are in the truck.

Look!
The dogs are in the water.

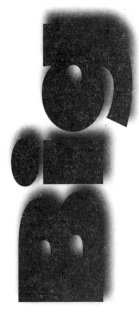

Big

Written by Wiley Blevins

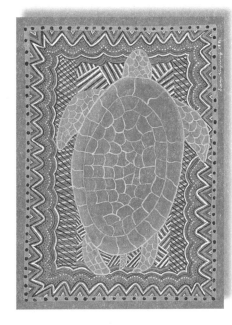

Scholastic Inc.

**New York Toronto London Auckland Sydney
Mexico City New Delhi Hong Kong**

Copyright © 2000 by Scholastic Inc.

SCHOLASTIC, HIGH-FREQUENCY READERS, and associated logos and designs are trademarks and/or registered trademarks of Scholastic Inc.

Puppy Carrying a Pheasant Feather by Yi Om

I see the puppy.
It looks little!

I see the elephant.
It looks big.

Circus Elephant by Dame Laura Knight

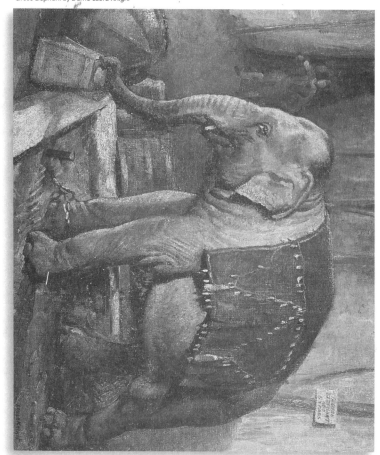

untitled by Susan Wanji

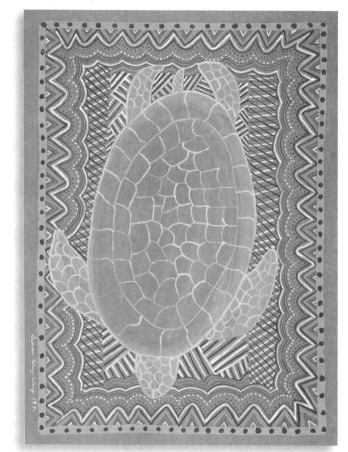

I see the turtle.
It looks big.

Fresco of a camel from the Church of San Baudelio de Berlanga. The Metropolitan Museum of Art, The Cloisters Collection, 1961

I see the camel.
It looks big.

I see the horse.
It looks big.

Le blanc-seing (Carte Blanche) by René Magritte

I see the lion.
It looks big.

The Sleeping Gypsy by Henri Rousseau

I see the cow.
It looks big.

The Yellow Cow by Kishi Ganku

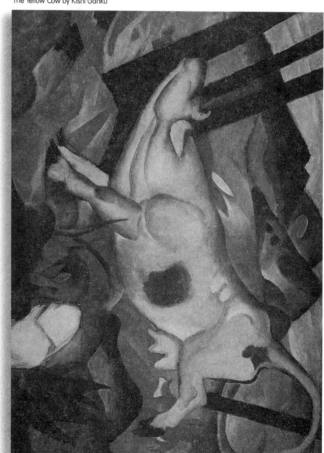

IN THE Forest

Written by Melissa Schiller

Illustrated by Margaret Kasahara

Scholastic Inc.

New York Toronto London Auckland Sydney
Mexico City New Delhi Hong Kong

4 5 6 7 8 9 10   23   05 04 03 02 01 00

I see the forest.
What do you see?

What do you see?
I see a tree.

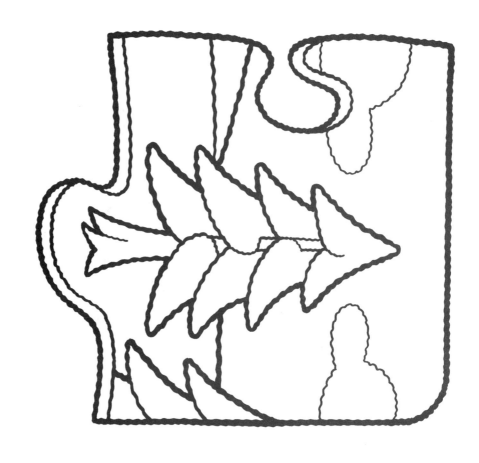

❷

What do you see?
I see a squirrel climbing up a tree.

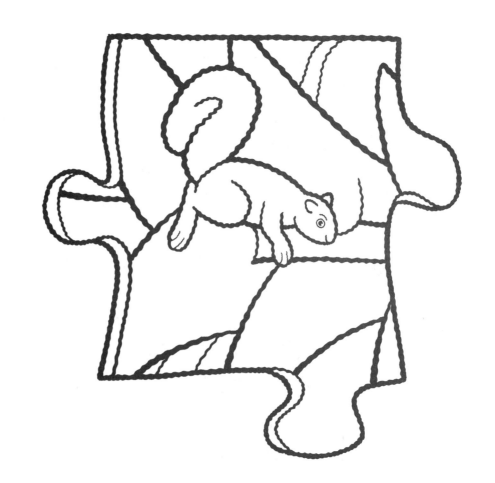

❼

What do you see?
I see a deer drinking water.

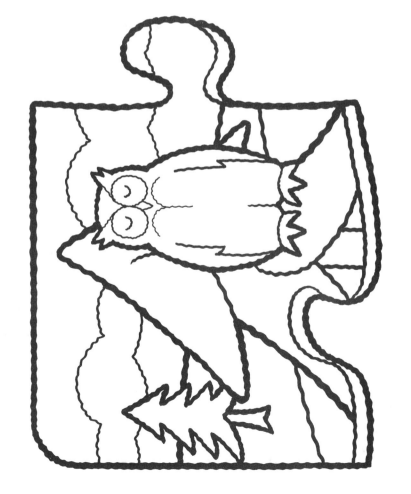

What do you see?
I see an owl sleeping in a tree.

What do you see?
I see a rabbit in the grass.

What do you see?
I see a bear eating berries.

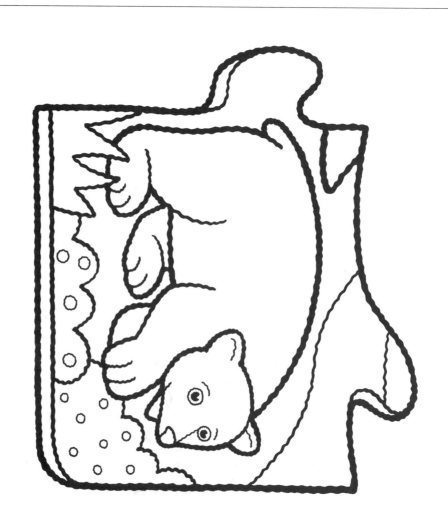

We Like to Play!

Written by Ellen Tarlow

Illustrated by Luisa D'Augusta

Scholastic Inc.

New York   Toronto   London   Auckland   Sydney
Mexico City   New Delhi   Hong Kong

4 5 6 7 8 9 10   23   05 04 03 02 01 00

What do we like to do?
We like to play!

What do you like to do?
I like to draw.

What do you like to do?
I like to paint.

What do you like to do?
I like to dig.

What do you like to do?
I like to pour.

What do you like to do?
I like to pull.

What do you like to do?
I like to push.

What Is It?

Written by Ellen Tarlow and Wiley Blevins

Scholastic Inc.

New York Toronto London Auckland Sydney
Mexico City New Delhi Hong Kong

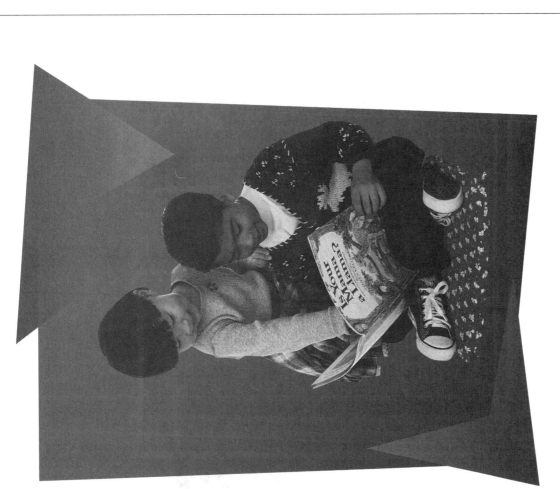

Is it fun?
It is!
What is it?

Is it a pan?
Is it a pig?
What is it?

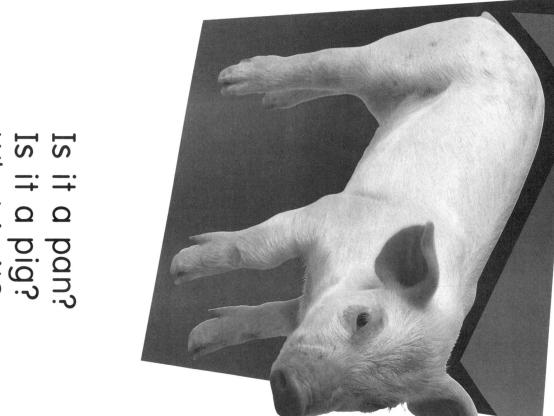

Is it a can?
Is it a cat?
What is it?

Is it a hat?
Is it a hen?
What is it?

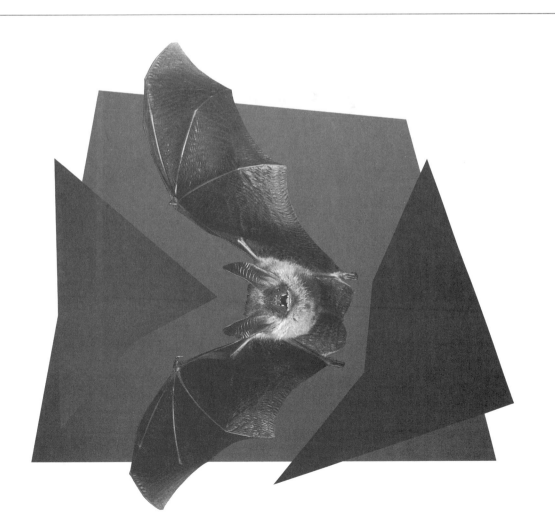

Is it a bat?
Is it a rat?
What is it?

Is it a top?
Is it a pot?
What is it?

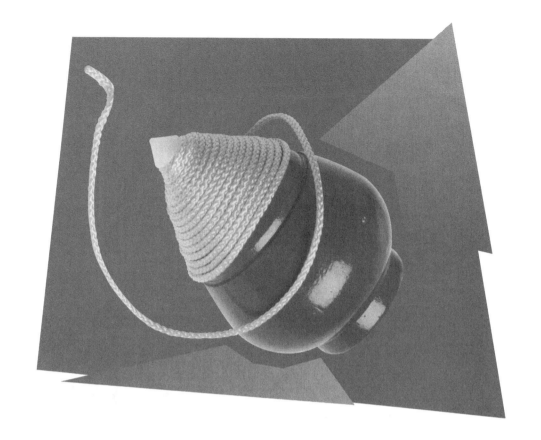

Is it a man?
Is it a mop?
What is it?

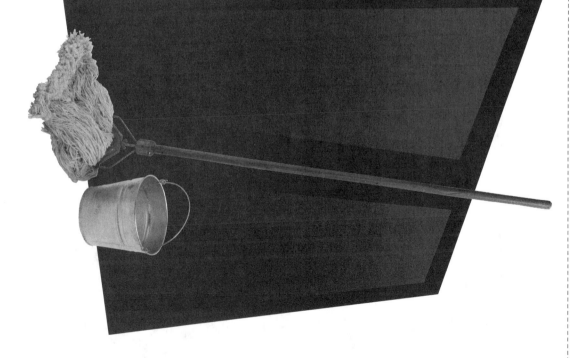

School

I see crayons.

I see scissors.

I see books.

I see desks.

I see chairs.

I see children.

I see school.

Lunch

I like apples.

I like sandwiches.

I like bananas.

I like pizza.

I like cookies.

I like milk.

I like lunch.

I Like

I like to wake up.

I like to eat.

I like to read.

I like to write.

I like to ride.

I like to hug.

I like to sleep.

I Am

I am running.

I am jumping.

I am building.

I am climbing.

I am dancing.

I am swinging.

I am sleeping.

I Can See

I can see a red ladybug.

I can see a brown bear.

I can see a yellow snake.

I can see a gray elephant.

I can see a green frog.

I can see a black whale.

What can you see?

Kittens

Can you see 1 kitten?

Can you see 2 kittens?

Can you see 3 kittens?

Can you see 4 kittens?

Can you see 5 kittens?

Can you see kittens?

I can see kittens!

Dogs

My dog can walk.

My dog can jump.

My dog can catch.

My dog can sleep.

My dog can sit.

My dog can swim.

We like dogs!

The Band

Can you see the guitar?

Can you see the drum?

Can you see the horn?

Can you see the harmonica?

Can you see the triangle?

Can you see the kazoo?

Can you see the band?

We Are Painting

We are painting green grass.

We are painting 5 red flowers.

We are painting 4 orange butterflies.

We are painting 3 blue birds.

We are painting 2 black horses.

We are painting 1 yellow sun.

We are painting!

We Can Go!

We can go.

We can go to the the library.

I can go to the mountains.

I can go to the

I can go to the desert.

I can go to the

I can go to the North Pole.

I can go to the ocean.

I can go to the jungle.

We can go to the moon!

Can You See It?

Can you see it?

I see a rooster.

Can you see it?

I see a pig.

Can you see it?

I see a dog.

Can you see it?

I see a horse.

Can you see it?

I see a mouse.

Can you see it?

I see a skunk.

We see animals!

We Like Fruit

We go to the store.

I like apples and oranges.

I like oranges and pears.

I like pears and peaches.

I like peaches and bananas.

I like bananas and strawberries.

We like fruit.

My Cats

My cats are on the chair.

My cats are on the rug.

My cats are on the washer.

My cats are on the stairs.

My cats are on the table.

My cats are on the bed.

My cats are on me!

Look!

Look! The dogs are in the tub.

Look! The dogs are in the garden.

Look! The dogs are in the truck.

Look! The dogs are in the water.

Look! The dogs are in the mud.

Look! The dogs are in the sand.

Look! The dogs are in the tub.

Big

I see the elephant.

It looks big.

I see the camel.

It looks big.

I see the lion.

It looks big.

I see the cow.

It looks big.

I see the horse.

It looks big.

I see the turtle.

It looks big.

I see the puppy.

It looks little!

In The Forest

What do you see?

I see a tree.

What do you see?

I see a deer drinking water.

What do you see?

I see a rabbit in the grass.

What do you see?

I see a bear eating berries.

What do you see?

I see an owl sleeping in a tree.

What do you see?

I see a squirrel climbing up a tree.

I see the forest.

What do you see?

We Like to Play!

What do you like to do?

I like to draw.

What do you like to do?

I like to dig.

What do you like to do?

I like to pull.

What do you like to do?

I like to push.

What do you like to do?

I like to pour.

What do you like to do?

I like to paint.

What do we like to do?

We like to play!

What Is It?

Is it a pan?

Is it a pig?

What is it?

Is it a hat?

Is it a hen?

What is it?

Is it a top?

Is it a pot?

What is it?

Is it a man?

Is it a mop?

What is it?

Is it a bat?

Is it a rat?

What is it?

Is it a can?

Is it a cat?

What is it?

Is it fun?

It is!

What is it?

Readers Log

Student Names

High-Frequency Reader										
1. School										
2. Lunch										
3. I Like										
4. I Am										
5. I Can See										
6. Kittens										
7. Dogs										
8. The Band										
9. We Are Painting										
10. We Can Go!										
11. Can You See It?										
12. We Like Fruit										
13. My Cats										
14. Look!										
15. Big										
16. In The Forest										
17. We Like To Play!										
18. What Is It?										

I	see
like	to
am	a
can	you

my	the
we	are
go	it
and	on

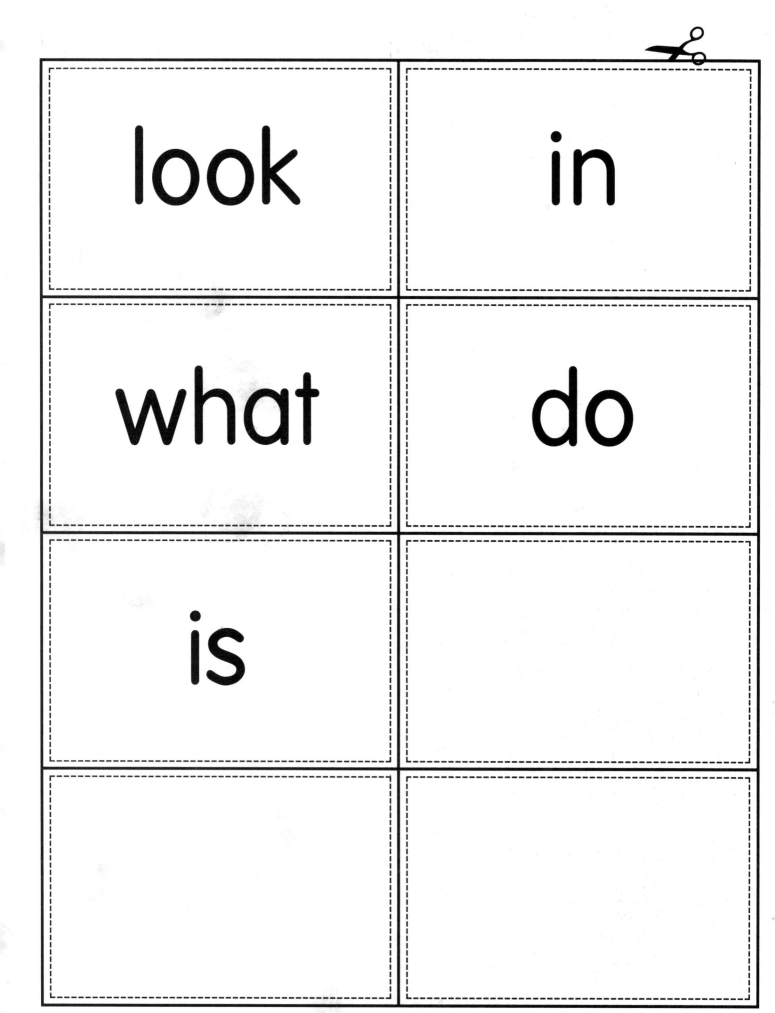

look

in

what

do

is